Uncovered Voices

Uncovered Artistry is a non-profit community interest company, based in Glasgow, that celebrates the creativity of survivors of domestic and sexual abuse. We are founded on the belief that creativity and entrepreneurship can be healing and empowering.

Abuse and trauma is a multi-faceted problem in Scotland and the UK — no two stories are entirely alike. And yet, in coming together to share these stories, we can recognize many similarities and patterns. The *Uncovered Voices* project aims to empower survivors to find the words for their experiences; share their writing with one another; recognize that these stories are both unique and subject to broader societal problems; and feel encouraged to pursue arts in the future as both a financial means and a means for emotional recovery.

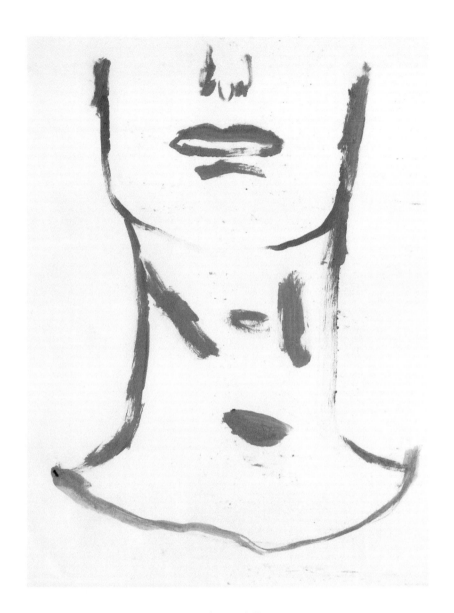

Ailsa Sutcliffe

NADINE AISHA JASSAT

In her essay, *The Transformation of Silence into Language and Action,* feminist writer Audre Lorde asks: 'What are the words you do not yet have? What do you need to say?'[1] It is a direct question, and a remarkable one for the reader: to suddenly turn inwards and ask ourselves what we are holding within us, what words exist underneath our silence. Lorde acknowledges the fear that keeps so many silent, but points too to the opportunity held in speaking out. She reasons that, while fear may be present in silence *and* in speaking, it is speaking which holds the potential for connection and change, both within ourselves and those around us. Lorde knew the transformation that could come in the telling — in the finding of voice and using it to articulate self, experience, and truth — just as she knew that the alternative, the weight of silence on the person who needs to speak out, could be unbearable.

It is with a similar understanding that Uncovered Artistry come together. They are a Community Interest Company who recognise the link between storytelling and survival, between speaking out and healing. Their mission is to empower survivors to find the words for their experiences, precisely because they understand the power held in the naming and telling of the story. Consequently, Uncovered Artistry channel their energy, efforts, and resources together to invest in helping survivors to tell their stories: whether through workshops, online campaigning, or publications such as this one. And they do so within the context of a global movement towards speaking out and bringing the truth from behind closed doors, turned away faces, and under heavy carpets, out into the open; whether it is via social media movements such as '#MeToo', the rise in grassroots activism groups, or the sounds of thousands of voices taking to the streets to protest in Women's Marches across the world.

For many survivors of sexual violence, layers of experience are often marked by voice and voicelessness: whether it is the violation of what was said to or about you; the feeling of voicelessness at having your power taken away; or being spoken over, unheard, or not believed; or whether it is the journey of reclaiming your voice, freeing it, and beginning to tell your story. And it is no small thing to do, to open a door which for many was long held shut — whether by trauma or fear or the voices of others — and speak. And yet, it is an act which every individual in *Uncovered Voices* has done, a bravery every single person here has summoned in order to come together and tell us: Listen. I need to speak. I have something to say.

---

[1] *From The Transformation of Silence into Language and Action , available online via genius.com : https://genius.com/Audre-lorde-the-transformation-annotated (last accessed September 2018).*

The need to speak, and the role which feeling silenced and finding voice play, are key throughout *Uncovered Voices*. We find it in the 'retelling what's untold' in Axe Marnie's 'Plagiarized'; witness it in the journey from feeling 'like a book bereft of words' to the resilient reclamation as 'a book waiting to be written' in M.L.M's 'The Gambit'; hear it in the singing of Bee Parkinson Cameron's heart in '2012'. This is an anthology of testimony and telling: from the photo collage bearing witness in M.J.L's 'Our Streets', to the sense of a story unfolding with each stanza in Peter Callaghan's 'Family Snaps', or the imagery in Tabatha Stirling's 'Fake', which as much shows the story to us as tells it.

Uncovered Voices presents a multitude of voices coming together, bound by Ailsa Sutcliffe's artwork which runs through the anthology like a spine, each image translating another snapshot of the story: from the throat, which opens this collection as if about to take a breath, to Ailsa's closing image, and the sparks which emerge from a figure's head like the sun, like the power of our own thoughts, wisdom, or memory. *Uncovered Voices* powerfully demonstrates the ability of art to translate and tell experiences. Trauma is illustrated here not in abstract words such as 'dissociation', 'grief', 'flashbacks', but instead told using language and imagery which shares the reality of survivor's experiences; the activating of 'auto shut off', the 'dismembered emotions', and the 'repeating waves' which bring the need for 'repeated acts of survival'. And yet, this anthology is as much about sexual violence and trauma as it is about healing and survival, as Beti Scott Brown reflects: 'these lungs are home to scream and song'.

The writing and artwork in this anthology narrate experiences of trauma and the journey to healing — a seemingly gentle word — as one that takes courage and strength. They convey to us a sense of self held in the speaker who brings themselves to these pages, and who lays out a map before the reader, dotted with the individual landmarks and steps of their journey: an aunt's kitchen table; streets that feel mapped on to the body; a cloudless blue sky filled with a warming sun; the opening stiches of embroidery that begin a story; realising 'Me, too'. Follow these journeys, reader, through the map of words, stories and truth that you find here.

We may be years later and miles apart from where Audre Lorde first spoke this forward's opening question, however, the question of what we need to say, the words we need to find, resonates and echoes still. Today, with this book in your hands, you hold the words that many survivors needed to speak, and need you to hear. Listen to them, consider them, and honour them — in the courage and power behind each line. And remember, as Lorde says: there are so many silences to be broken.

Nadine Aisha Jassat

CONTENTS

Axe Marnie

Salted Marrow

Every one of my bones
will break
if you say my
name again.

At dinner time we
do not speak,
but he salts
his meat
like snow
and the sound when
he bites down
breaks the glass
stuck in my throat.

I swallow and
digest the sand
nourished now I can
break his hand

Low res

soft purple at the edges
changing in age
wanting to get sharper
but fading away
thumb prints on your skin
careless attention
damaged cells
on a low resolution

Plagiarized

I am a cursed object
I am a back broken locket
I am a goblin held up under
the downtown bridge
earning my doctorate
I am the axe, the hatchet
I am the axis and the fist
triggered like a fuckboy
I go off scripting from a kiss
retelling what's untold except
where I was there it was
therefore this cross on
my working says Plagiarism,
your stories so attention grabbing
you can't be serious
but better that than
an attack of the humours
tragedy plus time creates a golem,
Adams rib tickling and solemn

IT'S BEEN FIVE
WEEKS AND I
CAN STILL SEE

THE GHOSTS
OF BRUISES ON
MY THIGH

Ailsa Sutcliffe

C l a i r e   A s k e w

Show Me Again

Show me again
how to take you home
— Karen Solie

I've forgotten how to be the woman
I thought I was

Show me again

the baltic 2am
tears freezing on my skin
his t-shirt blown against my ribs
his smell
like a bomb-lifted wall
and I said then I'd never be the woman
who did that to someone

Show me again

moving away from a past full of men
who should have known better
I said *everything*
on my terms
and meant it at the time

Show me again

finding letters my dead
grandfather wrote about me
his *bright, brilliant girl*
cornered by the wash house wall
sun loud as a trapped cat
and I'm still glad
he died on the cold boards of pain

Show me again

how I said I'd walk out on anyone
who held me

down or stilled me
after then

Show me

how I ran here apparently
backwards
in the dark
with no map
landing
in my aunt's kitchen
with one bag and £3.29 in the bank

and she says
again?
and I say
again

Christopher's Rules for Skimming Stones (Which are Also Rules for Living)

You have to be willing to get
your feet wet, he said – *get close,*
get in its face – as though this
were some tiered stadium
with floodlight and fake grass –
not Rydal on an autumn day,
Chris wading off to ankle-
depth and raising silt, Loughrigg
chucking its bracken net
of reflection onto the lake.

I laced my fingers
with slate chips and skated in
like a woman preparing to drown,
and recall he put his jacket
round me – the sort of slight, kind
thing that happened 'til the list
of unkind things got written.
Of my ten or so selected stones,
he threw away six: too big.
You shouldn't pick up anything
that doesn't fit in your palm.

I remember those rejects
settling at our white feet –
his a little paler – four
weird fish keeping still
under ripples – his jacket
smelled like cedarwood
from the cabin bed he built
and lived in, all splinters
and two-by-four that clicked
under our moving weight.

Pay attention, he was saying,
showing me his jack-
knifed arm and index finger,
the follow-through that came
after the twist. And the stone
splashed over Rydal's foxed
and silver mirror – seven,
eight, nine – Chris counting in
a song that never began.

He'd use those same deft
hands in anger, and I'd bolt
into a night as unreliable
as Lakeland scree. But at Rydal
that day he said to *try,*
and keep trying, and I counted four,
then five and each time
waited to see if he'd smile.
You have to let go lightly, he said –
now, I wish I'd reminded him.

You have to get down low and look
at where you want the thing to land,
then put it there. He closed his fingers
round my wrist, against the pulse.
He put the perfect missile in my hand.

Things Men Want to Hear You Say

Mostly, yes. *Yes* – as they press
themselves into you, and yes,
true, sometimes you agree, they're
doing okay, but then, what else
can you say when they ask
if it was good for you but *yes?* And yes,
too, is the only response to the book,
to the meal, to the piece
of jewellery you wouldn't have bought
in a million years, *I loved it, yes.*
Do you want to come
up? Can I call you
back? Do you see what
I mean? Are you listening? *Yes,*
yes, yes   I'm all ears, I'm
all sex, I'm in silk seamed stockings all
the live-long day – my legs
are aching, my girlfriends texting back
and forth: *I know, I know.*
I have to go and find myself a little
piece of something else, though
it may kill me – I'm walking
into its cold and scary
terrain. I hope
there'll be a yellow room, with
one bare bulb, a single bed
too hard for sex, a door that I can close
on *yes, of course, don't worry, I'll*
be fine. The walls of that room
will be built out of *stop,* and *I've*
never liked that you do that to me,
and I will lie down with my own *I'm tired*
and *don't* and *that's not fair*   though
not before I've turned the key
in the lock, put out
the light, and welcomed in the kind
and private dark, whose name
of course – *of course!* – is *no.*

Tabatha Stirling

Long Way Home

It's a long way home
To the cats, the barns, the belfry's
Rape-seed gorges and ever-distant voices
To the dusty halls and houses
And you.

It's a long way home
To the view of saffron from our tiny hill

A message in damson, the Fisher's regal bill
And to the total, utter thrill
that's you.

Bales and dragonflies plus twice-kissed wine
Seeds, pollen, and nothing that was ever mine
Picture-books bulging in pockets
For nostalgia raids
And my particular addiction withering with
each day for you.

We were a weary autumn storm
That pissed on rusty love.
And the bats, the cats, the poison
and the blackend mess of reason
of spite and gin and heathen
that's you.

It's a long way home
To a creamy moon & shell-pink yarrow
Names that entangle tongues, the roar of salt & shadow
To the love, the hate, the marrow
Of you.

Fake

my cheek razor burned by the
hallway carpet.

it might have been burgundy once

we play a symphony of hurt.

the rip of silk
my bruised cunt
he gobs in my face
I conjure hexes

hunted breaths

grinding me into silence.
Let me be clear that I am screaming
despite the tie you have crammed
in my mouth – sodden with spit
and rage.

The most distinguished of my father's
friends and so ugly with your socks
rucked around bony, blue ankles,
pimpled arse bobbing in time
to my rape.

then
I curl and freefall
into another tunnel of blackred hurt

but

I know this pain
from a bedroom stuffed with
sindy dolls
long time
past

Wipe yourself with a Kleenex
And make hushed small talk the
way people do in that difficult
pocket of silence
after a church service

i am carbonated
a yield of artificial crops
IamIamIam

i am compelled to sink my teeth
into your tiny softness

so I do.

Whose streets?

These streets are my streets. I walk to work on these streets, I walk back home. I walk to work, home, work, home. I go anywhere I need to on these streets. The shops, the cinema, the occasional nice restaurant. I stand on these streets waiting for friends. I carry my umbrella, I tie my shoelaces, I yawn in the early morning rain.

I'm walking to work. Somebody leers at me from the bus stop. His relentless gaze drilling holes into my flesh, filling my footsteps with dread.
Every step I take.
I'm walking to work. An old man decides it's time to comment on the way my hips move. Swinging hot.
Every move I make.
I'm walking to work. And a group of lads are about to run me over with their car.
Every step I take.

I'm walking home. The streets are empty now. But not too empty for 'Hey love, give me a kiss.' They never seem to be too empty for that.
Every step I take.
I'm walking home. It is dark. I try to glance behind me discreetly. Check enough, but remember, don't check too much. Don't show your fear.
Every move I make.
I'm walking home. Behind me a certain kind of car engine is being rammed. It is raging, racing, roaring. The dread finds me again. The car isn't here yet, but my body already knows. I've been spotted by men. And then 'Die you whore!'

Every step I take, every move I make, I am reminded that as a woman, simply existing in public can be exhausting.

The streets in this collage are mine and not mine. You see, they are all streets I walk down daily and they are all streets I have been harassed on. Sometimes, I want to wear a t-shirt listing all my physical attributes so men don't need to tell me what they are. Believe me, I know myself. Instead, on too many days I wear tears over my eyes from all the comments I never asked for. So yes, I have swinging hips, I have red lips. Did you go home and imagine me stripped?

Enough! I am enough. I strip the tear-torn veil from my eyes and find my sight red hot with resistance. As my tears meet my hands, I turn them into a burning grip. You keep staring at my lips, or my hips and I will take this grip and wrap it tight around your gaze to extinguish it.

Every move I make, every step I take, I am reminded that as a woman, simply existing in public can be a radical act.

These streets are my streets. Every step I take, every move I make I take up space.

M.J.L., 'Our Streets'

Bee Parkinson Cameron

2012

I was a smart girl and I always said that I would protect myself, that I wouldn't become one of those women abused by men, that I would be wiser than that. I thought I'd be able to spot an abuser a mile away and I was wrong. I held my hand out to touch his hand, little knowing at the time that when I pulled him into my home and into my heart, that I was pulling a demon with a human face and a bewitching smile.

I ignored the darker parts of him that I knew were lurking beneath the surface. I convinced myself that his concern for where I was and what I was doing and who I was with was just general concern for my wellbeing. After all, I had experienced depression and a touch of alcoholism in the past. He had seen the scars on my thighs. It was only natural for him to ask so many questions, to check that I really was okay. It was only natural for him to want to be with me, to be selective with who I spent my time.

When his temper started to build and he lost control, I was curling into the pillows, desperate for some protection. I was scared of what would happen next, I was scared that his anger might grow to the point that he became blind to anything and everything around him. He must have seen my stricken face, the tears drying on my cheeks. He relaxed and took me into his arms, reassuring me that I was safe and that all would be well. He just had a bad day, that's all. He was struggling at work, it was a job that was becoming too much for him. Human faults, we all had them, and even I lost my temper and screamed like a banshee at times.

It was when he started to touch me in my sleep that I knew something was really wrong. I had been sexually assaulted when I was twelve years old, my first kiss non-concensual, and he knew this. I had been honest about all my experiences, and I had hidden nothing from him. I had opened my heart to him, bared my soul for him to see. He knew it all and he knew that my fear would paralyze me.

After that first night when I lay frightened in the dark as his hands moved to claim every part of me that he could, he said that he had been unaware of what he was doing. It happened again, and again, and I told him that it wasn't right. I told him what he was doing and he claimed it was 'sexomnia'. He was doing it in his sleep and he couldn't stop it.

When you think you are in love, you are willing to believe anything that your lover tells you. In this instance, what would I rather believe? Sexomnia? Or that he was deliberately doing this to me? That he was hurting me?

Every day, I woke up in the morning, I showered, ate breakfast, prepared my lunch and went off to work. I worked and read books on my lunch break. I came home, I ate my dinner and watched some television and then I went to bed. I was scared of sleeping because I knew what was likely to happen. It was happening far too often and I didn't know what to do. This was warfare the likes of which I had not been trained to deal with.

Whenever I have spoken about this with anyone, I have always maintained that if he had hit me, I would have been able to deal with that better. If he had hit me, I would have been able to hit him back. But this, this was something else.

I would struggle to wake from a sleep induced by prescription drugs only to find his hands roaming across my body, and that was on a fair enough day. I would be able to slip out of the bed and escape. I would scrub my skin just that little bit harder in the shower that morning. On bad days, I would wake up to the sharp pain of him inserting himself inside me. I was stretched and I felt sick as he moved inside me and when I slipped out of bed on those mornings, I would lock myself in the bathroom and I would sit on the toilet and try not to cry, my hand on my stomach as I felt the semen dripping out of me. When I felt well enough to move, toilet paper bunched in my hand, I would wipe and there would be vivid scarlet blood glaring against the white tissue. On those mornings, I could barely glance at myself in the mirror. On those mornings, I tipped my head back and let the water wash over my face. I needed to be cleansed.

The pattern continued. My world became a living nightmare and there was fog all around me. My mind was in a place of perpetual confusion and I knew that this was wrong, that what I was seeing and feeling all around me was wrong but I didn't know what to do. It all became too much for me and I went to the doctor, my abuser with me. He didn't like me going to medical appointments or seeing doctors alone. I walked away from the doctors with a prescription in my hand and I had no idea that when I started taking those little pills, they would prove to be my salvation.

Within days of the doctor's visit, the fog in my mind cleared and I felt more like myself again. I looked at the world around me and I saw everything for what it was. I looked at this man, this manipulative, pitiful excuse for a man who had taken the love I had given him and had given me nothing but pain and misery in return, and I found a strength within me that I had long since forgotten was there. I told him that enough was enough and despite the sobbing and tears that came from him that night, I told him to leave. I put him on a train back to his mother's and I told him that there was nothing he could do to stop this, we were finished.

The police took initial statements and attempted to build a case against him. I had to do one of the hardest things I have ever had to do in my life. I sat for hours with the sexual offences liaison officer and told her in depth what had happened to me, when he had done it, which part of his body he had put where. But as the abuse had occurred behind closed doors with no witnesses and I had not been able to go to a doctor after the rapes had occurred and because he wasn't confessing to his crimes, they were unable to proceed any further with prosecution. I was sickened and I still am sickened to this day that the law could allow this injustice to occur. But I am so thankful to the police officers for their assistance to me in my time of need.

As I write these words now, I stand a woman who is proud to say that despite my suffering, I survived. I still experience flashbacks to this day, and it feels as though I am going through it all again, my body physically reacting, but I grit my teeth and clench my fists and think about pineapples and my heart sings softly to me *you are loved, you are loved* and when the moment passes, I look up into the cloudless blue sky with the sun warming my skin and I know that I am free.

I WAS PAINFULLY AWARE OF THE FACT I WAS UNSHOWERED

AND WASN'T WEARING A BRA

Ailsa Sutcliffe

H . B

One Survivor with Two Stories

He was a stranger, I knew him.
I begged for help, I didn't utter a word.
Screams, silence.
Strangulation, gentle hands.
Struggling, frozen.
The taxi driver watched, we were alone in my room.
It was my first time, it was my second.
I bled, I bled.
Africa gap year, University.
He talked to me the next day, I texted him the next day.
I thought he would kill me, I thought he would brag.
Fear, confusion.
"Mzungu", "slut".
Disappeared, three years.

Yet so much the same:
blood running down the drain
shower after shower
screams into pillows
burning eyes
rumours
flashbacks
panic attacks
......silence....silence....silence.

Peter Callaghan

Family Snaps

The sun sank when he came home.
Curled up on the couch
cushioned in cartoons
and giggles, I jolted

from my mother's side
when his silhouette
staggered past the window
like a twisted marionette.

Clambering and cowering
upstairs, I prayed for silence.
But plates crashed, blinds rattled,
door handles bore holes through walls

And once an ashtray
shattered the fish tank.
The neighbours heard everything
but said nothing. A broken man

he fell up the stairs
to his cold king-size bed
and rocked our foundations
with his snoring. Downstairs

a cigarette
burned like a beacon
in the flickering blue
of a muted cartoon.

The sun sank
when he came home,
now it rises in his eyes
when I go back.

Mum plays house,
dad plays hide and seek
and ready or not,
I play dead.

Rosie Tallant

Dream Catcher

Five months on and I tell myself it's over now.
It's only a memory,
you can't get to me,
you're a bump in the road
that stretches back behind me
and soon I won't see you there at all.

But it's five months on and the dreams still come.
Catching in the threads of my mind,
weaving themselves into all my days,
reminding me that you're still out there,
and that you're still in here
and I don't know how
to get you out.

Perpetrator

He was a PhD student
a Star Wars mega fan
an engineer, a class clown, a board game geek.

He was a funeral director
a world traveller
an artist, a hiker, a manga reader.

He was a café owner
a university drop out
a joker, a foodie, a red wine drinker.

He was a father
a shoulder to cry on
a nice guy, a good friend, a first-person shooter.

"RUSSIAN NEWSPAPER TELLS
WOMEN TO BE PROUD OF
THEIR BRUISES"

Ailsa Sutcliffe

Catherine Whittaker

Wet Feet

The surface shimmers
dancing light
attracting your gaze.
You get your feet wet
but do you dare
to step in, whole?
Will I be too cold?
You cannot see through
my broken waves.
Ever wavering you
what's your move?

Lesley O'Brien

Silence of her Song

High above the pines, high above the pines,
she lies cradled by birch
asleep in the forest, where giants have searched
hush weeping willow, hear the silence of her song
yes, hush weeping willow for the people who have gone.

High, sweet and silent she sings, high, sweet and silent she swings
tear drops salting her lips
awake in her dreams, with her darling she sits
hush weeping willow, hear the silence of her song
yes, hush weeping willow for the people who have gone.

High, through the mountains she blows, high, through the mountain she goes
greylags flocking to sleep
washing her cares, while her secrets she keeps
hush weeping willow, hear the silence of her song
yes, hush weeping willow for the people who have gone.

High like the eagle she soars, high like an eagle she soars
spirit flying by night
raising her hopes, a sacred starlight
hush weeping willow, hear the silence of her song
yes, hush weeping willow for the people who have gone.

John Brewster

Compendium

On that cloud-infested day
in summer when the rain
squirms like tree snakes
shaken from the leaf-tops,
the box retreats from the attic.

The sun overwhelmed,
water and mischievous air
have free rein, thumping boots
into glassy puddles of loft light,
vexing the cantankerous dust.

Downstairs, the box is laid out
like afternoon tea or begrudged
corpse, dependent on the thanks
shown, the awful bother caused.

Compendium, mouths the boy
as the word curtsies before him.
With no semblance of a beginning,
of a time when it was not tattered

or demonically absent of elements,
the box succumbs to attention,
exhibiting its exotic lexica: Ludo,
Chinese Chequers, Solitaire.

The vinegary tang of old cardboard
dematerialises, leaving a colony
of square paper coffins, crammed
with counters, beads and effigies.

The secret doctrine of gaming
unveils: pieces lead to peace.
Rules of abuse can be broken.
The silenced boy at the big table
wins by letting go of the dice.

When the loud adults return,
the wound-up clock chiming in
and the raked fire grumbling,
even when the box is shut up,
the boy, poker-faced, plays outside.

Max Scratchmann

#MeToo

And then it confronts me,
Me too,
me,
as a fresh faced kid
and the kindly man who offered me a lift,
when at the midway point
between the town we'd left
and town yet to be,
where either way involved a long, long walk,
he stuck his hand on my crotch and

said: *You can tolerate this, cant you?*
A confident grin on his cheery Santa face;
or the mentor who invited me to his house
to discuss my writing and
eulogised about being able to paint
and paint me in the nude,
cornering me as he
suggested that I undress anyway
to see if inspiration struck.
And the countless others
who called me dear or love,
the hands that strayed all over me
in concert queues
and art first nights,
the offers of overnight accommodation
that came along
with suggestive looks
and leers.

And, yes, these are old hurts,
the scars long healed
if visible still,
so,
as a man,
I'm not invoking that Me Too hashtag,
or asking for your thoughts and prayers,
but still letting you know that it's
#NotAcceptable
#NoWay
#NotAgain
#NotOnMyWatch

Julie Tsang

A Sinking Hole

If the ground opened up
a sinking hole
I'd give in to its pull
I'd gravitate deep down
swallowed
into a black abyss

You'd be searching
tearing up the room
all teeth and claws
to no avail
I'd watch you from below
You can't see me
You can't see me

Your rage colossal
still I hide
curl into a ball
it's instinctive
the only way I know

Your sound seeps away
escapes my ears
drowned out
silenced
I float away

In the blackness I dream
of another place
another home
a gentle smile
to call my own

I dream of fields, green and vast
sun warm on skin, cut grass, children's laughs
free from the monster
the despair and woe
I'd cover my footprints
no tracks
you can't find me

And as quickly as I was swallowed
I'm thrown back up

your voice resounds
smashing my ears
fists hammering
the room reverberates
You see me
You see me
teeth gritted
claws out

But it's over for now

You scarper off
I'm left on the floor

Searching for the hole
to take me away once more

Fiona Black

The Eggshell Dance

I get home late, the door's ajar
the widescreen telly shows the bombs,
the oil-rich smoke, the blackened sun.
You do not move, you stare at scuds
and follow fireworks in the sky,
the broken men and tanks and cars;
your headphones keep the world at bay
and in the peace you watch the war.
I tiptoe in, my eggshell dance, my desperate fear of losing you.
I do not care for Cap Ferrat, feel no desire for luxury.
I have no wish for gems and jewels, I walk away from champagne bars
and stumble in designer shoes, the awkwardness of wanting you.

I watch you there absorbed by death,
a tabloid famous billionaire.
The beginning of the end they say
but not close to our end at all.
We too are subject of attention,
a photograph, some column inches,
we're not what's called a great romance
more bickering and sniper fire.
I gag on oysters salt and sweet and struggle with my need of you,
I do not stay to share your wealth and paparazzi startle me.
I miss old quiet and easy ways, my casual friendships disallowed
my family's weekly phone-call barred, the loneliness of loving you.

The Leaving Do

I'll keep schtum when you go
and try to forget
the midden you made.

The hidden invoices,
the overloaded sockets,
the charts sliding down the wall,
        the papers stacked like Himalayan ridges.

I've held my rage as you bark orders,
refuse help, dash futures, let secrets slip
fail us with indecision.
You're a debt, an overage,
a liability but now you're off
Huzzah! Hoorah! Let's celebrate.

I helped, you know.

They pushed, I shoved,
tripping you up by questioning motives,
querying expenses, mentioning extravagances,
the clutter, the mess, my doubts …

revenge, for that wandering hand
as I sat,
        new and nervous,
                on my very first day.

HOW CAN YOU
DEFEND THIS

Ailsa Sutcliffe

M . L . M

The Gambit

Everything that I was you took from me
You left me empty and afraid
like a book bereft of words
a day with no light

You perverted my empathy
ensnaring me
The wire trap tightened by my own submissiveness
baited by my guilt
triggered by my desire to please

Misdirection was your weapon
and I was the magician's accomplice
Love and happiness were the illusion
skillfully delivered
the audience captivated by your charm

Every word was carefully chosen
every action had a hidden purpose
The odds were always stacked against me
you dealt me a hand I could never win
You held all the aces

Like a delinquent alchemist
you took the most precious part of me
and turned it into ash
My spirit left covered in detritus
from years of neglect and misuse

Eroded like a sea battered coast
crumbling piece by piece
I was lost in the murky depths
searching for a way to breathe
to resurface and survive

From somewhere deep within came
the final deception
the last turn of the cards
that was mine to win the game

Everything I am you made me
Resilient and unafraid
a book waiting to be written
the warm glow of sunrise and the promise of a better day

Semantic Error

The Big Bang
It was a defining moment
The name sounds sudden, cataclysmic
but no one knows how long it took
to create the critical circumstances that
resulted in life as we know it

I don't recall it happening –
my conferred laryngitis
Slowly I became a TV on mute
and you chose not to read the subtitles
But when I spoke to someone else,
then

Then you heard every word
twisting them into a confession
your malicious accusation
designed to shield your indiscretions
short circuited my reasoning
overwhelmed my ability to breathe
There was no primordial response

Like a badly dubbed film
all meaning was lost in translation
When I said 'no'
you heard 'well maybe, try asking again'
When I said 'no'
you heard 'if you apologise and tell me you love me'
When I said 'no'
you heard 'ok'

I'm sorry caller we cannot connect you

My words did not reach you
as you told me how much you loved me
My words did not reach you
as you told me it would prove we loved each other
My words could not reach you
muffled in your arousal
My words did not reach you
but perhaps my tears did

My hot cheeks were cooled by the fabric –
the new mask you gave me
I tried to find comfort in its refuge
but your volume was up full

a cacophony flooding my senses
I could not escape
Even the pillow betrayed me in the end
refusing to steal my last breath
instead sheilding you
Reality and your conscience remained strangers

Now entering power saving mode

I didn't hear you
when you asked if I was alright
I didn't hear you
when you asked why I was upset
I didn't hear you
when you said you were sorry
I didn't hear you
when you said you felt like you raped me
I didn't hear you
I didn't hear you
as auto shut off activated

Awake? Perhaps

Awake? Perhaps
Asleep? Not quite
Where is this place I find myself?
It has many different forms
images like mementoes of times past, lost
Random and disjointed
flowing vividly
only vaguely familiar
Whose life is this?
unfolding like an uninspired narrative

Dismembered emotions,

in fear but not afraid
joy marred by sadness
hope consumed by doubt
hurt without pain
An observer;

Yet this life is mine
somehow forgotten
suppressed by existence
marked only by the passing of time

A

Autumn

I am alive with colour
I burn, I rage, I tremble, I shake, I bow, I break

you might see the falling, but I stand tall.
Drawn to the glow, you took the warmth for yourself,
sent me up in flames and didn't stay long enough to look.
But I was sure to take it in, this mess you made.

Burnt, yet still alive with colour.

I grow tough now, my roots reach further.
Cut me open and count each ring,
each one a moment, a memory, a hope.

I am hundreds and thousands of rings.
I am my sisters, my mother, my grandmothers.
We stand tall together, a forest burning in autumn.
We burn, we rage, we tremble, we shake, we bow, we break

Cut us open, count our rings,
feel our shared rage, our wisdom, our strength.
We stand together, we stand tall,
alive with colour.

Protect and Survive

I'm under the table
Thatcher's nuclear fall-out shelter
Protect and Survive
The foetal position
The nuke going off
in my kitchen
but not the one she's
warning us of

I'm under the table
back curved
limbs bent
drawn to the torso
and I rock gently
Outside my table
an angry face on me
Block it out
Hold my pain and rock
curled up in my comfy
pre-born position
I'm humming quietly

The medical profession
point me out
in a diagram
Ah…
The foetal position
You can see how
the figure reacts
to minimize injury
to the neck
to the chest

So I'm in my comfy
pre born position
waiting to be born
I can play dead
I can escape the
withdrawal of my drug
I can ward off bears
I can do anything
but live with this

I hug my knees closer
my head bent in
I breathe
I warm
my heart
my liver
my lungs
my kidneys
in this position
But I will never again
warm to you.

I don't like curry

I like my mother's homemade soup
but not on the wall
I like chocolates for Christmas
but I never get any
I like making cakes
but you don't like them
So I never do –
make them for us
I don't like curry
but you know that
don't you.

If I say it,
my skin
will be stained yellow
for days
and I will stand
in the shower
washing away
the aftermath
of saying
"I don't like curry"

Ailsa Sutcliffe

Eilidh, Linda, and Pamela

A collaboration from Lorna Hill's group at Women's Aid
East and Midlothian.

The Thing Is

The thing is
I feel slightly lost today
I still need wisdom from Women's Aid
I'm grieving over things
I thought I'd already grieved

The thing is
I felt weaker and weaker
I lost my friends, my independence
I wanted to be this special person
loved by who I loved

How did this happen to me?
Dad taught me to work hard
to be a good person
I am a horse of war
    Keep on plodding
          Keep on carrying
               Keep on avoiding ambush

The thing is
I am stronger than I think I am
I have told the truth
I tell the truth
Your lies will always come undone

I am strong, I am wise, I am love
My time is blossoming
yours has gone
You're a void
just someone I used to know

Beti Brown

Stitching Survival Into Existence

A body of text is born of a simple repeated stitch.

This body, like my own, is a site of duality; of damage and reconstruction, of injury and healing, of oppression and resistance.

These cells are site of pain and strength
These lungs are home to scream and song
This body is space for trauma and healing

Repeating waves of trauma remind me of the need for repeating acts of survival. Simply being here is an act of survival. Laughing, loving, and — when I need to — crying and hating are all acts of survival. Anger is valid and an act of survival. Contemplation, meditation, prayer — acts of survival. From the mundane to the profane, living with trauma is an act of survival.

I'm not always so assured of this. That's why I commit these thoughts to text(ile). I gravitate towards craft skills associated with women and femininity, because of this association these skills are disregarded and undervalued; their power underestimated. Through the textile practices of my recent and distant ancestors I connect with my fellow survivors of gender-based and sexualised violence. Beyond space and time, our voices together are stronger, as if harnessing the power of ancestors. As it says in one of my favourite songs of struggle:[1]

> As we go marching, marching
> Unnumbered women dead
> Go crying through our singing
> Their ancient call for bread

Repeating stitches create repeating words create repeating phrases. Each stitch is a rejection of the masculinist logic that devalues textiles and other 'woman's work'. Each word is a refusal to be silenced by acts of violence and by a society that doesn't care. Each phrase is a reassertion of my narrative, my truth, my autonomy and my power.

If self-doubt creeps in, I stitch, in the hope that in my hands the stitched words will crystallise into the affirmative power that I need.

I pray (to anyone who might hear) that survival is the act of resistance I need it to be

These are the words I need to hear and need to say. Sometimes they are words of vulnerability; desperate pleas that I can stitch my survival into existence. Sometimes they

---

[1] *Bread and Roses, a poem by James Oppenheim — based on a speech made by feminist trade unionist Rose Schneiderman the worker must have bread, but she must have roses too. The poem was later set to music by Mimi Farina.*

are assertive, direct – a slogan. Sometimes declarations of anger, a political banner. Sometimes words of affirmation to myself and my siblings in struggle.

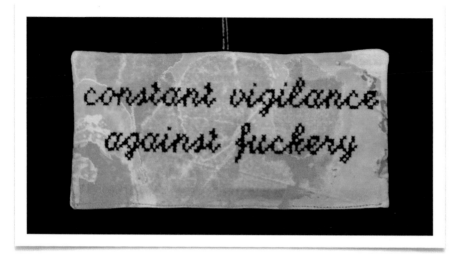

Constant vigilance against fuckery

Always an act of resistance. Always taking up space and refusing erasure. Always informed by an understanding of the violences that have been perpetrated against me as seen through a wider lens. Knowing the systems of domination, control, exploitation and oppression which not only allow for abuse, but rely on it for their maintenance.

Considering the deeply engrained cultures of sexual violence, the societal and institutional barriers we as survivors face, the scale of the problem, and the vast numbers of us who live with trauma, I feel overwhelmed and depressed and, at the same time, galvanised and strengthened. We live in sad solidarity with each other, but connection with someone through shared trauma is still a connection. When we connect ourselves with other survivors, we reject the all-pervasive myths about violence; the individual bad apple, the man in the bushes, the victim who is to blame. Our collective survival is our most powerful tool in the fight against oppression. By crying together, laughing together, screaming, marching, healing together, we not only actively resist against the violences that have been done to us personally, but we resist against the systems of power and privilege which lurk in the background of our histories.

Sexual, domestic and gendered violence; heteronormative, homophobic and transphobic violence; racialised, imperialist, xenophobic violence; ableist violence; classist violence – all of these violences can be drowned out by a collective declaration of survival and resistance.

We will survive

Our individual and collective survival is the best 'fuck you' to the people and forces who caused us so much pain. We can reject attempts to destroy us by living boldly, by constantly healing, and by seeking justice in whatever form it takes.

For a while, I was preoccupied with thoughts of revenge; of smashing windows and breaking bones, of locking up and throwing away the key. But no prison sentence, no amount of broken bones or bricks through windows could ever address the harm that was done, could ever restore what was taken, or move me closer to healing.

Since this realisation, I have repeated the following phrase in my mind, in several textile works, in conversations with friends and with strangers. It gives me strength and a reason to continue when stopping feels like the only option.

Survival is your best revenge.

NADINE AISHA JASSAT is a poet, writer and creative practitioner. She is the author of *Still,* a feminist poetry pamphlet, the editor of *Rise:* an anthology of writing from YWCA Scotland – The Young Woman's Movement, and her work has appeared widely online and in print; including in *New Writing Scotland,* The British Council's *Discover* Project, and 404 Ink's acclaimed *Nasty Women.* In 2018, she received a Scottish Book Trust New Writers' Award, as well as being shortlisted for the Outspoken London Prize for Poetry in Film and the prestigious Edwin Morgan Poetry Award. As a creative practitioner, she has delivered significant education and creative participation work in Scotland's gender-based violence sector, and she was named as one of '30 Inspiring Young Women Under 30' by YWCA Scotland. Her debut poetry collection, *Let Me Tell You This,* is forthcoming with award-winning publisher 404 Ink in Spring 2019.

CLAIRE ASKEW's debut poetry collection, *This changes things*, was published in 2016 by Bloodaxe. The collection was shortlisted for an Edwin Morgan Poetry Award, for the 2016 Saltire First Book Award, the 2017 Seamus Heaney Poetry Centre Prize, and the 2017 Michael Murphy Memorial Award. Claire is also a novelist, and her debut novel *All The Hidden Truths* won the 2016 Lucy Cavendish Fiction Prize and was published in August 2018 from Hodder and Stoughton. Claire is currently the Writer in Residence at the University of Edinburgh.

TABATHA STIRLING is a writer, poet and indie publisher living in Edinburgh, Scotland with her husband, two children and a depressed Beagle, called The Beagle. Her publishing credits include Spelk fiction, Literary Orphans, Mslexia, and Feminine Collective. She recently won the Scottish Book Trust 50-word short story competition and was awarded 2nd place in the NopeBook Halloween contest. An extract of her addiction memoir is to be published in the 'Wild & Precious Life' Anthology, edited by Lily Dunn. Tabatha is a member of both The Society of Authors and The Scottish Federation of Writers. Her debut novel, *Blood On The Banana Leaf,* is to be published by Unbound in 2019. Tabby is absolutely ready for a zombie apocalypse.

PETER CALLAGHAN graduated from the Royal Scottish Academy of Music and Drama in 1998 with an Honours Degree in Dramatic Studies. For the past 20 years he has worked as an actor, theatre-maker, corporate role-player and drama workshop leader.

JULIE TSANG is a playwright and poet. She was mentored with the Playwrights Studio Scotland in 2012. Recent credits include *Troon* at Theatre 503 in London and *Lilyburgh Lane* at Cumbernauld theatre, Glasgow, which was one of the recipients of the Scotland Short Play Award 2017. Julie is on the professional writers' programme with *Yellow Earth Theatre* in London, on a seed-commission to write a full length play. Julie's plays and poems have had readings at the Tron theatre, Traverse theatre and Soho theatre. Julie's poem *My Body Bleeds* is published in a collective of spoken word poets by Merchiston Publishing.

JOHN BREWSTER is a writing tutor, belongs to the Scottish Book Trust's pool of authors, and is a Scots Patron of Reading. His writing has appeared in various publications and won a number of prizes. *Automatic Writing*, a full-length collection of his poetry, was published in 2015 by Cultured Llama.

LESLEY O'BRIEN has worked for Glasgow Women's Aid for 25 years, has been a registered Storyteller since 2005, and sings in several bands including *The Carlton Jug band*, *The Moonbathers* and *Kittlin*. Lesley loves to combine stories, poetry and music, as a Creative Writing facilitator, as well as in performance. Lesley is a firm believer in the power of creative words to stimulate good health and chaired Lapidus Scotland, for many years, promoting this cause.

M.L.M is a self-confessed wee blue weirdo from the Muppets era. She is a vaguely sporty, vaguely arty, animal loving, rpg gamer. Fascinated by movie production and visual effects, she is also a wannabe avid reader/writer. Her best skill — procrastinator extraordinaire.

MAX SCRATCHMANN is a well-known British writer and illustrator. His poems and short stories have appeared in many anthologies and magazines, and he runs the Edinburgh performance poetry company, Poetry Circus.

CATHERINE WHITTAKER is a teaching assistant in social anthropology at the University of Edinburgh. Her recently completed PhD thesis looks at 'warrior women', violence, and religion in an indigenous Highland Mexican community. Born 1988, she was raised in Germany by Italian and British-Australian parents. Her free time is devoted to travel, playing the piano, and singing jazz.

BEE PARKINSON CAMERON is a writer of poetry, short stories and plays currently working on building connections and relationships within Scotland's Creative Industries sector. Bee focuses on exploring love in all its forms, the oppositions of life and death and the nature of humanity and what it means to be human. She is passionate about issues such as mental health, domestic abuse, euthanasia, abortion and human sexuality. Bee's work has been published in several anthologies through 'collections of poetry and prose'. She has also produced two plays 'The Divine Comedy Show' in March 2017 and 'The Journey Home' a play about domestic abuse in November 2018.

BETI SCOTT BROWN is a survivor of gendered violence, queer and disabled. She is also an artist and community arts facilitator based in Glasgow. In her personal practice – under the name *Sister Stitcher* — she explores themes of healing, survival and resistance through fibre art; these works are influenced by DIY, feminist and craftivist politics, and are available online and at indie craft and zine fairs. Through both her personal and professional work, she hopes to connect members of marginalised and oppressed communities, as well as contributing practically and creatively to movements for social justice. Find her @SisterStitcher on Instagram for more.

M.J.L is an aspiring artist and writer in the midst of establishing herself in Scotland. Having strengthened her feminist praxis through study and direct action, she looks to use her work to rail against patriarchy and its intersecting oppressions as well as to celebrate the healing creativity can bring to people's lives. In her day job, she supports tenants to exercise their rights and talk truth to landlord power.

AXE MARNIE is an emerging writer and artist based in Edinburgh. They identify as a high school and college drop-out, genderqueer performance poet, painter, dancer, play writer and comics maker trying to make friends while making ends meet. Previously published in *The Stinging Fly* and *Strange Alters*.

FIONA BLACK has spent much of her life moving from place to place fulfilling the demands of working in theatre and television production. She has recently returned to Scotland and plans to take more time to write.

LINDA, EILIDH, PAMELA, AND LORNA HILL

'The Thing Is' was written by Linda, Eilidh and Pamela during a creative writing workshop at Women's Aid East and Midlothian. The women's collaborative work was inspired by the poem 'The Thing Is' written by Ellen Bass. This session was led by Dr

Lorna Hill who is a researcher, writer and creative writing facilitator. She runs bibliotherapy workshops for women who have been affected by domestic abuse. This work has been nominated in The Write to End Violence Against Women Awards.

H.B works as a nurse in Scotland, painting and going for long walks to relax. H.B lives happily with her husband, son, and little bump at present. She never thought this family would be possible following her experiences and PTSD, and chose only to tell her husband of her experiences written here. Writing 'One Survivor With Two Stories' has helped her to voice the experience again and she appreciates Uncovered Artistry for giving her a voice on the matter.

ROSIE TALLANT is an occasional poet and wannabe story teller who spends more time thinking about writing than actually writing. She originates from Bradford in the far off land of Yorkshire, but now lives in Glasgow. She moonlights as a yoga teacher and loves baking, attending protests and playing video games.

TRISH BRYCE is a visual artist and poet who comes from Edinburgh.

A is a Master's student based in Glasgow, researching global feminist movements. As a survivor of sexual violence, journal writing and poetry have provided a creative outlet for her over the years. She participated in the Uncovered Voices workshops, her first experience of publicly sharing her work. Her poem, 'Autumn', was inspired by a walk through Kelvingrove park on her way to one of the workshops (listening to Kesha's Praying and firing herself up into an autumnal rage). Writing has become a powerful tool in her non-linear road to healing.

AILSA SUTCLIFFE is an art tutor, care worker and part-time illustrator based in Glasgow. She spends most of her spare time with her cats, bringing them up to be strong, independent women.

RUBY ALLEN, designer of the anthology cover, is based in Glasgow, UK. She enrolled on a BA in Sculpture and Environmental Art at The Glasgow School of Art in 2018. The cover is illustrated by hand with inks, chalks and watercolours.

A special thanks to the Forest Quarterly Arts Grant, The Scottish Book Trust, and the Scotmid Co-operative Grant for funding the printing and promotion of this anthology.

QUARTERLY ARTS GRANT

The Forest is a collectively-owned, volunteer-run community arts space and café in Edinburgh, Scotland. Its quarterly arts grant supports local and international artists pursue creative projects by offering financial and other support. To learn more, visit http://blog.theforest.org.uk/grants.

Scotmid's Community Grant scheme helps deserving causes across Scotland. In the last four years, we have supported hundreds of projects which have touched the lives of people living in the communities we serve. Chances are one of them was in your own community! The maximum amount available for a Community Grant is 500 pounds. To learn more, see https://www.scotmid.coop.

Book Week Scotland is an annual celebration of books and reading run by the Scottish Book Trust. The Scottish Book Trust offers grants every year to five Young Programmers who are funded and supported to put on an event for Book Week Scotland. They look for applications from young people (18 – 26 years) who wish to pursue a career in the literature sector. It is a great opportunity for young adults to gain experience of programming and put on an event around a topic/area that interests them. To learn more, visit www.scottishbooktrust.com.